Anybody for M

A Play

Brian Clemens and Dennis Spooner

Samuel French – London
New York – Sydney – Toronto – Hollywood

ANYBODY FOR MURDER?

First presented at The Mill Theatre, Sonning, by Sally Hughes on 22nd August, 1989, with the following cast of characters:

Max Harrington	Robert East
Suzy Stevens	Emma Myant
Janet Harrington	Linda Jean Barry
Edgar Chambers	Barrie Gosney
Mary Ticklewell	Jacqueline Clarke
George Ticklewell	Keith Smith

Directed by Douglas Argent
Setting by John Elvery

CHARACTERS

Max Harrington
Janet Harrington
Suzy Stevens
Edgar Chambers
Mary Ticklewell
George Ticklewell

The action takes place in a converted farmhouse situated on the remotest peninsula of an equally remote and tiny Greek island

ACT I
SCENE 1   Morning
SCENE 2   Early evening
SCENE 3   Late that night

ACT II
SCENE 1   The next morning
SCENE 2   A few minutes later

Time—the present

Note: It is suggested that, before the curtain rises on Acts I and II, Greek bazouki music be played.

It is not imperative that Suzy Stevens be red-haired—she could be brunette, or blonde, and the dialogue amended accordingly.

ACT I

Scene 1

The main, ground floor area of a converted farmhouse. The farmhouse is situated on the remotest peninsula of an equally remote and tiny Greek island. It is early morning

The conversion has turned the original farmhouse into something closely resembling the more conventional holiday villa. This main area has been gutted to provide space for cooking, dining and living

Centre back are french doors, wide open to a small patio; beyond this is a backdrop of wide sky, and the suggestion of arid, rocky ground leading away to cliffs, and eventually, the sea. In front of the french doors is a breakfast table; adjacent to it is a tiny kitchen area with a working surface, pantry cupboards, a small sink, a waste-bin, etc.

Downstage L are some steps leading up to a kind of mezzanine-level gallery; off this gallery are the doors to the master bedroom and bathroom. Both gallery and stairs are part of the original structure, and have terrazzo floors; at the top of the stairs is a small rug. Also a small table with a vase on it. At one end of the gallery is a window

Further downstage, and L is a door leading to the guest-room. The stairs partially screen someone at this door from seeing fully the body of the main area. We presume that a bathroom is en suite with the guest bedroom

R is a door under the gallery, leading into a tiny workroom. The main area is furnished with a sofa, chairs, a small bureau, a drinks cabinet and a small table bearing a vase identical to the one in the gallery, but all these items have been shipped from Britain, there are only a few items of Greek bric-a-brac in the area—which feels relentlessly British

Somewhere in the area a coffee percolator bubbles merrily

The stage is empty, then the workroom door opens and Max Harrington enters, carrying a small paper bag. Max is an attractive man, who has natural charm, cares about his appearance, and is a womanizer. There is something altogether furtive about him as he looks up at the closed bathroom door, and then moves to the table that is set for breakfast. He picks up the sugar bowl, looks around, sees a decorative bowl nearby, and moves to pour the contents of the sugar bowl into it

Suddenly Janet Harrington, wearing a robe, comes out of the bathroom on the gallery. Janet is Max's wife; an attractive woman with long blonde hair. She has a slight lisping impediment of speech that causes her to say her "r's" as "w's"—this allied to her air of wide-eyed innocence, makes her seem more naïve than she actually is. It also tends to make her seem vulnerable, and very likeable indeed

Max presses back into cover under the gallery as Janet moves towards the bedroom

Janet exits into the bedroom

Satisfied that she has gone for the moment, Max re-emerges into the body of the room again—picks up the now empty sugar bowl and pours the contents of the paper bag into it. He now pours the sugar back into the bowl again, stirs it with his finger and places the sugar bowl back on the table. He regards the sugar bowl—then moves it so as to be nearer one of the place settings. He is still regarding this when . . . Suzy Stevens enters through the french doors. Suzy is a bit of a bombshell, young, attractive, sexy, with a superb figure shown off to advantage by the wet swimsuit she wears. Her hair, long and blonde, is wet too, a chunk of seaweed adheres to her swimsuit. She is shivering

Suzy Max.
Max Suzy! You're much too early. I haven't done it yet!

Suzy tries to speak through chattering teeth

And you're all wet—that wasn't part of the plan. You were supposed to be *rowing*, not swimming!
Suzy The wig blew off . . . (*She pulls off the long blonde wig to reveal her short red hair beneath*) I had to go overboard and get the damned thing! Max, I'm freezing.

Max, with constant looks up at the closed bedroom door, urges Suzy to the guest bedroom

Max The guest room! You'll find towels in there. Stay out of sight until it's over.
Suzy Max——
Max (*overriding*) Janet'll be down any minute.

Max pushes Suzy into the guest bedroom—and as she goes, the seaweed drops to the floor outside the door

Suzy exits

Max very agitated, closes the door, and then he sees the seaweed and reacts. As he picks it up . . .

Janet enters from the bedroom. She still wears her robe

Janet Max Harrington, you're up to something!

Max spins round and stares up at Janet

I heard you, rattling around in that den of yours at six-thirty this morning. And what on earth is that you're holding?
Max This!? Why it's seaweed of course.

Janet Seaweed!? (*During the next exchange she descends the stairs*)
Max Yes, I ... I read about it in the *New Scientist* ... It can be processed into fertilizer ... and if it can, I intend doing it ... and spreading it on our own personal piece of desert out there.
Janet Darling, you never give up, do you? Mmm, that coffee smells good. (*She moves to pour herself a cup of coffee*)

Max watches her then hurries over to pick up the sugar bowl

Max Sugar, darling?
Janet You *are* up to something.
Max (*reacting, waving seaweed*) Darling, I *told* you——

Janet takes her coffee and ascends the stairs again as:

Janet (*interjecting*) Preoccupied then. You know very well I never take sugar in my coffee.

Janet exits into the bedroom

Max remains. A moment

> The guest bedroom door opens and Suzy appears, still wearing just a swimsuit

Suzy I can't find any towels!
Max In the drawer!
Suzy I've looked in the drawer!
Max Then try the top shelf of the cupboard——
Edgar (*off*) Max?!
Max Oh, Lord! It's Edgar—get back in there! (*He thrusts Suzy back into the guest room*)

Suzy exits

Max closes the door—just in time

> Edgar Chambers enters through the french doors. Edgar is tall, spare and eccentric, a man who always looks untidy

Edgar Max?
Max Edgar!

Edgar walks right past him—and over to a small cabinet which he opens to take out a bottle of ouzo and a glass

> Edgar you can't stay here! It's gone eight thirty. The ferry will arrive any minute.

Edgar waves him aside—pours himself a glass of ouzo

> It's the third Wednesday of the month, Edgar, *your* turn to make the trip to the mainland. You *are* going to the mainland?

Edgar, having drained his glass, shows some signs of recovery, then starts to recharge his glass

Edgar The ferry's late. I saw it on my way here, still more than a mile off shore ... won't get here for another ten minutes at least. I'll catch it all right.

Max seems relieved

(*He sips his drink and then adds*) That's if I decide to go.
Max If!? But you've got to go.

Edgar stares into his glass

What's wrong? Why are you drinking so early?

Edgar fully regards Max for the first time

Edgar I've done it, Max. I've committed my murder.
Max But that's marvellous news!

Max urges Edgar towards the door

You must tell me all about it when you get back.
Edgar (*pulling free from Max*) The whole Wilson family, Max. I killed them all. Even Grandma. And all thanks to you.
Max (*still intent on getting him out*) Oh, I just gave you some technical advice, that's all.
Edgar No, no you gave me more than that. You gave me an untraceable poison ... I won't be getting rejections on this one—the publishers will be beating a path to my door. This is going to make me thriller writer of the year. I'm on my way, Max.
Max I hope towards the ferry.
Edgar Eh?

Janet enters from the bedroom—dressed now, in beach jacket and shorts

Janet Edgar! Aren't you going to miss the ferry? (*To Max*) It *is* his turn, isn't it?
Max He's just leaving.

Janet descends the stairs

Edgar I had to drop by and tell you the good news.
Janet Good news? Edgar, you haven't!?
Edgar I have. The whole Wilson family. Even Grandma. In Chapter One.
Janet Oh, really well done, Edgar.
Max Yes, yes ... now, Edgar, the ferry ...
Edgar I'm thinking of drowning Jennifer.
Janet Who's Jennifer?
Max Jennifer's the governess ... now look, if he's going to catch that boat——
Janet (*overriding*) If she's anything like my governess was, drowning would be too good for her ... boiled in oil more likely.
Edgar But she wouldn't be rowing in oil.
Janet Who's rowing?
Edgar You were. That's what gave me the idea.
Max *Edgar.*

Janet *I* gave you the idea?

Edgar Well, these past couple of days, when I've seen you out rowing around the headland——

Janet Me? Rowing? Why would I be rowing?

Max Seaweed.

Janet Seaweed?

Max Darling, I already told you ... (*To Edgar*) I'm working on a new tack—convert seaweed into fertilizer—then perhaps I can come to grips with that moonscape out there.

Edgar (*to Janet*) So that's what you were doing, collecting seaweed?

Max The ferry, Edgar. The ferry.

Edgar Ah! Yes. Be back tomorrow ... (*He starts to hurriedly exit through the french doors*) We can talk more about drowning, *and* I've got a decapitation in mind!

Edgar exits

Max sighs with relief—then moves to the table

Max Thank goodness!

Janet (*regarding him*) Why on earth did you let Edgar think I go out rowing?

Max Anything to get rid of him——

They sit down to breakfast, Janet in the seat nearest the sugar bowl

—I don't think I could have taken decapitation with my cornflakes. Besides, I was looking forward to breakfast with just the two of us.

Janet You haven't said that in a long time. In fact there are lots of things you haven't said—or done—in a long time.

Janet now takes the sugar bowl and liberally scatters sugar on her cornflakes. Max stares at her intently—she glances up—he "covers" with a smile. This done, she adds milk. She picks up her spoon to eat—he waits tensely—and then, she lowers the spoon again

I saw Suzy Stevens just now.

Max *What?* (*He turns to look at the guest room door*)

Janet Least I thought I did—this morning from the bedroom window. I saw a girl swimming off the headland, a girl with short red hair—just like Suzy Stevens. Of course, it couldn't have been her.

Max Of course it couldn't have.

Janet After all, what would she be doing here? You promised you'd never see or contact her again.

Max And *we* promised never to discuss her again.

Janet I'm sorry, it was seeing that girl just now, brought it all back.

Max Darling, I had a brief affair ...

Janet Brief? It went on for a whole year.

Max But it's over now, all in the past—now come, let's enjoy our breakfast. *Please?*

Janet (*starting to eat*) Do you regret moving here? I mean, it was basically my idea, and you threw up a promising career ...

Max Darling, I was a second-class research chemist in a third-class job.
Janet But the reason for coming here —starting our own vineyard hasn't
worked out ...
Max Maybe not yet, but it will—you'll see.
Janet Darling, you're always so optimistic ... and I've every confidence
that you'll come up with the answer soon. (*She now collapses unconscious—her face in the cornflakes bowl*)
Max (*regarding her coldly*) Sooner than you think! (*He rises, moves to fling
open the guest room door wide*)

A beat, then Suzy enters, wrapped in a towel, sans wig

Suzy. Darling.

They kiss passionately—then Suzy breaks the embrace

Suzy Don't you think you should lift her head out of the cornflakes? It
could ruin the plan if she's found with milk in her lungs!

*Max moves to lift Janet's head and leaves her propped in the chair. Then he
moves back to Suzy again*

Max Darling we've done it.
Suzy Not yet. She isn't dead yet.
Max No, but she'll be asleep for quite a while. And when she wakes up
she'll be dead. (*Elated now*) And then, in a month or two, the insurance
will be through and I'll be ten thousand pounds richer. *We* will. Then it's
goodbye to this "mature vineyard with great potential" ... Look at it—
fifty acres of Gobi Desert—the only thing that'll grow out there are
pyramids.
Suzy But you'll sell it off, won't you?
Max Yes, I might get lucky and find another mug—or a homesick Arab.
Suzy Max, let's get it over and done with.
Max OK. You'll need the wig.

Suzy nods and exits into the guest bedroom

*Max takes the sugar bowl into the workroom then emerges and takes Janet
out of the chair, lays her on the ground, and strips off her beach jacket, to
leave her in halter top and shorts*

*Suzy enters from the guest bedroom, just finishing adjusting the blonde wig
on her head*

Max tosses her Janet's jacket, which she puts on

Now, let's make sure we haven't overlooked anything. We'll take Janet
down to the bay and hide her behind a rock. *You* will then get the boat—
you'll be wearing the wig and her jacket so that——
Suzy (*interjecting*) If there *are* any tourists sailing off shore——
Max (*interjecting*) They'd swear they saw a woman with long, blonde
hair—moving—very much alive! Then, once we are sure the coast is *really*
clear—we prop her up in the boat ... wedge her in——

Suzy Push the boat out.

Max The current sweeps it out to sea—and five or six minutes later, one of these little chaps goes to work. (*He produces a bunghole*) A soluble bungplug.

Suzy It melts away, water floods in.

Max And both boat and Janet descend gently to the ocean bed. Which is rather apt, because she'll be still asleep.

Suzy And when they find the body——

Max Which, the way the currents run around here, may not be for weeks— months even—there won't be much left to identify. Perfect.

Suzy You've thought of everything.

Max The successful murderer has to. (*He reacts*) That's funny.

Suzy regards him

"Murderer". That's the first time I've consciously thought of it like that. That's what we are, isn't it? Murderers.

Suzy I prefer ... lovers.

They embrace

How do we get her down to the bay?

Max Wheelbarrow along the lower road.

Suzy But that passes right by your neighbour's place.

Max He's away. We have the whole island to ourselves. Come on.

Suzy and Max lift Janet and exit through the french doors

There is now a pause

Mary (*off; suddenly*) Yoohoo! Yoohoo!

A pause—and then Max and Suzy enter backwards through the french doors in a hurry—still carrying Janet

(*Off*) Yoohoo!

Suzy Who is it?

Max I don't know!

Suzy *What are we going to do!?*

Max Quick!

They quickly take the body and place it down behind the sofa

At that moment, Mary enters. Mary Ticklewell is a gushing, rather prepossessing woman who is dressed in black more for an upper-middle-class mourning in Esher, than for the arid heat of a Greek island. She is panting somewhat

Mary Janet Harrington? Yes, of course it is; slim, attractive, blonde. That nice, kind neighbour of yours was very specific. But of course, George got the directions mixed up as usual ... *insisted* it was the other house, *refused* to climb the hill until I made sure. And you must be Mr Harrington? George will be so pleased. (*She extends her hand*) Ticklewell. Mary Ticklewell. Been dying to meet you.

Max (*finally*) We ... we ... haven't met, have we?
Mary Not till now. I'll go and fetch George. You haven't met him either.

Mary exits

Suzy and Max regard each other—stunned

Suzy She thinks I'm Janet.
Max Well, we'll have to play along for the moment! (*As he speaks, he moves back to Janet's body and lifts it up*) Come on, we've got to get her out of sight.

Suzy helps him lift the body—and they move towards the nearest door—the guest bedroom

No, not there—the lock's broken—upstairs, in her own room.

Max and Suzy start to carry Janet up the stairs

Suzy They'll know I'm not Janet.
Max Why should they—they're complete strangers? Anyway, you've been *pretending* to be Janet for the last three days.
Suzy Only from a distance.
Max Don't worry, don't panic, and I'll get rid of them as soon as I can.

Suzy and Max, carrying Janet, exit into the master bedroom

George enters on to the patio—he carries two huge suitcases—and now puts them down and mops his brow. George Ticklewell is exactly the kind of man one would expect to find married to Mary. Slightly pompous, resignedly hen-pecked, and also unsuitably dressed for this climate. He is panting hard. He wears a mourning patch on one sleeve of his jacket

Now Mary enters on to the patio—struggling with three smaller suitcases. She puts them down and gets her breath

As they move into the main area:

George Are you sure they'll let us stay?
Mary Well, George, I haven't broached the subject yet, but they're not barbarians, we're not dealing with your criminal classes, now. The ferry has gone, and won't be returning until tomorrow, and they are surely not going to let us spend the night out there—it looks like the Gobi Desert! (*She glares around the empty area*) If the truth's told, they're probably preparing a room for us now. And, George, I'm warning you—no matter how persuasive they are, we are only staying the one night. Two at the most. Ah!

Mary reacts as:

Suzy and Max enter from the master bedroom—he subtly locking the door behind him

There they are, George.

Suzy and Max start to descend the stairs towards Mary and George

Janet Harrington and ... er ...

Max Max.

George How do you do, we've come a long way to find you.

Mary And find you we have. And didn't I tell you, George—she couldn't be anything but a Thripton.

Suzy A Thrip-what?

Max (*suddenly realizing*) A Thripton, darling—remember—*your maiden name*—the name you had *before you became my wife*.

Suzy Oh, a *Thripton*!

Max That explains it then, you're old friends of the family.

Mary No. We *are* the family. Oh, but I don't want to anticipate George's good news.

All eyes turn to George who is a bit bemused

George. The *good news*, George.

George Yes, er ... um ... the good news. Um ... well, it *is* rather a long story ...

Max Oh, I hope *not* too long.

George This could be to your advantage. *Well*, yes ...

Suzy and Max sit down

(*He clears his throat several times*) Hum ... um ... ha ... well ... hum ... (*A sudden aside to Mary*) Are you sure *you* don't want to tell them, dear?

Mary Oh, do get on with it, George.

George Yes, quite. Well ... w—*ell*. (*A confident announcement*) In October nineteen twenty-four ... or was it November ... ?

Mary *George*.

George Yes, well ... in October ... *or* November, nineteen twenty-four, Jonathan, Wilmot, Thripton, left Southampton, on the *SS Luciana*, bound for the port of Buenos Aires. The weather on that day was particularly calm——

Mary (*overriding*) *George*! It's a long story—cut it short!

George Yes—well—to cut a long story short, Jonathan Thripton liked the South Americas so much that he decided to settle there.

Max (*on his feet*) Well, that *is* good news. Terrifically good news. Thank you.

George Oh, but there's more.

Max Oh!

George Jonathan Thripton prospered in those foreign climes—and then, three months ago ... (*Dramatically he stabs a finger on the black patch on his sleeve*)

Max He tore your jacket?

George *He died*. He died, apparently without an heir. But we know differently, don't we?

Mary Of course they don't know differently! George, *that* is supposed to be what you're explaining! (*She turns to Suzy*) Like you, my dear, I too am a Thripton ... second cousin to dear Jonathan whom I never met, but I am sure I would have liked! Go on, George.

George Mr Harrington, I am by profession a lawyer.

Mary (*quickly*) And a very good one—despite what his colleagues might say.

George (*drawing breath to continue*) What *do* they say?

Mary Get on with it, George.

George I think I have a right to know—if *people* are talking about me behind my back.

Mary George. (*She takes the initiative, and addresses Suzy*) The crux of the matter is that cousin Jonathan died and left some money, and it could be that you and I might be in contention.

Suzy Me?

Mary Well, you are the only other surviving Thripton we've been able to trace . . . and . . . well, I'll let George explain the dreary legal details.

George Do you understand anything about law, Mr Harrington?

Max Not much.

George Then allow me to lead you. There is some money involved here, and two possible beneficiaries. I am a lawyer, Mr Harrington . . . I know the way of these things. Two beneficiaries—*both* with an equal claim—and should they foolishly come into conflict . . . Litigation—claim—counter-claim—it could cost both parties a great deal of time and money——

Max (*interjecting*) You're here to do a deal!

George I am here to explore the possibilities of an out-of-court settlement to the mutual advantage of all interested parties.

Max That's what I said.

Suzy (*overriding*) Max?

Max What?

Suzy Don't you think *I* should go off rowing now?

Max Later, later. (*Back to George*) How much did he leave?

George Well, these things take time, things have to be proven.

Max Hundreds? Thousands? (*A pause*) *Tens* of thousands? Well?

George Millions.

Max Millions!? Millions!? (*Sudden afterthought*) Pounds or dollars!?

George Dollars.

Max Millions of dollars? Millions!?

George (*eagerly*) More than enough for everyone. So we *can* do a deal?

Max pauses, gathers himself, then, the old Max again, he turns to regard George

Max *Second* cousin.

Mary
George } (*together*) What?

Max Your wife's relationship to Jonathan Thripton . . . second cousin, you say?

George Yes.

Max And my wife's relationship?

George Well, nothing's been established . . .

Max Nevertheless . . .

George Mmm . . . er . . . you're asking me for an opinion . . .

Max But, George. Between relatives.

George Well, I ... er ... I'd hate to commit myself ...

Max Roughly. If *your* wife was his second cousin ... *my* wife was ... *what*?

George Well ... approximately ... *first*.

Max Approximately?

George The intricacies of the law, a claim such as this, it could take months ... years even, to definitely prove ...

Max Well, maybe *we* can speed up the process.

George Eh?

Max (*to Suzy*) I seem to remember lots of dusty old documents relating to you and your family ... tucked away somewhere. Worth a look, don't you think?

Mary I think it would be best to let George go through them. He'd be pleased to interpret them for you, and wouldn't even *think* of charging a fee.

Max (*overriding*) Oh, I think we can manage. Meanwhile, you'll obviously have to stay the night.

Suzy What?

Max Of course they will, darling, you know there's no ferry until tomorrow morning. You *will* stay the night?

George Just the one night. Two at the most!

Max Excellent. (*He crosses to the open guest bedroom door*) There's a bed made up in here ...

Mary Well ... well, that is very kind, but as my husband said ... just the one night.

Max Let me give you a hand.

Max, George and Mary cross to pick up their various pieces of luggage, and take them towards the guest bedroom. Suzy mouths "What's it all about?" but Max shushes her into silence

Mary I do hope you find those documents, Mr Harrington.

Max I'm sure we shall.

Mary I mean it would be *awful* if they were irretrievably lost ...

Max No fear of that.

Mary And ... er ... don't forget, we will be close at hand, should you wish to consult George about them.

George and Mary exit into the guest bedroom

Suzy (*after the door has closed*) For God's sake! Why did you ask them to stay?

Max Had no alternative, did we?

Suzy And what about *her*!? (*She points upstairs*)

Max She's fast asleep, and will be for most of the day.

Suzy And what when she wakes up?

Max She isn't going to wake up.

Suzy But surely—now *they're* here ... ?

Max Just trust me, darling.

She regards him. There is a pause

Suzy (*finally*) Well, let's go and get these damned documents then.
Max There aren't any documents!

Suzy reacts

But did you see his reaction when I told him there were!? I'd wager they
don't have a legal leg to stand on, and they know it. They're here to try
and cheat you out of your inheritance!
Suzy But, Max, it's *Janet's* inheritance!
Max Exactly. And, as far as they are concerned, you are Janet! Trust me,
darling—trust me. I have a new plan. A better plan!

The CURTAIN *falls*

SCENE 2

The same. Early that evening

*The stage is empty, then the workroom door opens and Max enters, carrying
two passports, pursued by Suzy*

Suzy Max, it isn't going to work.
Max It is. Look how neatly I've swapped the pictures in these passports.
Right down to new plastic sheet and an official stamp.
Suzy (*studying it*) "Chiddingbury Cricket Club"?
Max Only stamp I could find, but it only has to fool the Greek Passport
Control, and you know how lax they are. Especially if you're flashing a
deep cleavage, which you will be.
Suzy You've darkened Janet's hair down, haven't you?
Max Exactly, now she doesn't look unlike you—about as much as anyone
expects from a passport photo. And in this one, I've lightened your hair
up . . . so now, officially, she is you—and you are her. And when they find
her body, they'll find *your* passport along with it, with her picture in it.
Suzy But her hair's blonde.
Max It won't be when I've dyed it.
Suzy I'm confused.
Max Darling, it couldn't *be* more simple. Later tonight, we take Janet
out—the new red-headed Janet, carrying *your* passport, with *your* name,
and *her* picture . . . darkened down to match her new red hair. OK so far?
Suzy I think so. Why do I have to dye *my* hair?
Max Because, my poppet, as from this moment, *you* are Janet
Harrington—and you'll have *her* passport as proof of identity.
Suzy But with *my* picture in it.
Max Right! But her passport describes her as "blonde"—and we can't risk
a wig . . . not with this kind of money at stake.
Suzy All right, so I'm using her passport—what next?
Max We go ahead as planned—put her in the boat, push it out to sea . . .
with your passport alongside—and Suzy Stevens is officially dead. But

Janet Harrington—*you*—heiress to a fortune, and her loving husband—*me*—live happily ever after.
Suzy That's terrific, Max, that's better than we had before!
Max Many millions better. And not a flaw in the whole plan!

Suddenly, we hear the master bedroom door lock rattling

Janet (*off*) Max. Max!

Max and Suzy react

Max The drug must have worn off!
Suzy *What if she wants to see her passport?*
Max Keep calm. Keep out of sight ... and get me the sugar bowl ... (*He puts the passports on the table*)

Suzy exits into the workroom

Janet (*off*) Max. Max!
Max All right, darling ... just coming.
Janet (*off*) I'm locked in!
Max Of course you are.

Suzy enters and hands him the sugar bowl

He pushes her back out of sight. Then, sugar bowl in hand, he starts up the stairs

Coming, my darling. (*He gets to the master bedroom and unlocks the door*)

Janet enters, but remains in the doorway—she is swaying, semi-conscious

Janet Why was I locked in?
Max You ... had a fall. You ... you slipped on some seaweed.

Max urges her back into the bedroom and exits into the bedroom with her

Suzy remains, staring up at the bedroom

The guest bedroom opens and George and Mary enter

Mary We've decided to go for a stroll round the island.
George Just a stroll you understand—nothing more.
Mary Absolutely.
George My wife has discussed the matter, and explained to me exactly how I feel. Yes, you'll see no tensions here—no matter what the outcome of this legacy ... we are utterly sanguine ...
Mary George ...
George After all, it's not as though we are desperate for the money ... oh, no!
Mary *George.*
George No, winner take all is how we see it ...
Mary *George!* (*Then, sweetly between her teeth*) This is not a case of winners and losers ... but more an amicable agreement. Or, to put it another way ... an agreement amicably arrived at.

George Yes. (*Pause*) I'm not sure that is another way of putting it, dear.
Mary Let us go, George.

They are moving to the french doors now

George Ha, ha, ha . . . (*Sotto voce*) Was that carefree enough, d'you think?

Mary *George!*

George and Mary exit through the french doors

Suzy is left very bemused

A moment, then the bedroom door opens, Max enters and hurries downstairs

Max (*as he comes downstairs*) It's all right. I've got her under again. Had to force feed her. (*Then, warily*) Any sign of our guests?
Suzy They've just gone out for a walk.
Max Good. Bring me those bottles from the bench—and a bowl—I'll get on with dyeing her hair red. And we'll blonde yours too while we're about it . . . (*He hurries back up the stairs again*)
Suzy Max——
Max Hurry it up!

Max exits into the master bedroom

Suzy exits into the workroom and then enters a moment later carrying two bottles of dye—she glances around and sees a bowl. She hurries to pick it up

Edgar enters through the french doors, carrying two bottles of ouzo and a boxed orchid

Suzy turns, sees him, reacts with a gasp

Edgar Hallo. Is Max—Mr Harrington—around?
Suzy He . . . he's busy dyeing.
Edgar What?
Suzy Dying to get on with whatever he's busy at.
Edgar That's a pity. I wanted to tell him I know all about the murder now.
Suzy You can't know. How could you know?! We haven't done it yet!
Edgar You!? But I'm the one who's writing the book—it'll be *my* name on the cover. Edgar Chambers.
Suzy You're his neighbour!
Edgar That's right.
Suzy And you know his wife too?!
Edgar Of course.
Suzy (*shrieking*) *Mr Harrington!*
Edgar Oh, don't go disturbing him if he's busy . . .

Max enters from the master bedroom

Max Edgar! What are you doing here? You're supposed to be on the mainland until tomorrow morning. (*He crosses to the gallery, pulls aside the drapes and peers out*)

Edgar (*as he does so*) Had a bit of luck, met a young couple on their way to Corfu–they dropped me off *en route.* (*To Suzy*) By the way, who are you?

Suzy Me? I'm—I'm ... tell him who I am, darling!

Max A complete stranger. (*He closes the bedroom door and starts down stairs*)

Edgar Eh?

Max (*taking the bowl from Suzy and placing it casually on the drinks cabinet*) Suzy Stevens. She's something to do with theatre–calls everyone "darling", don't you, darling? Now you've got me doing it!

Edgar How did you get here, Miss Stevens?

Max She rowed.

Edgar Rowed?

Suzy Rowed?

Max How else could you have got here? Yes, she rowed. Definitely. To the wrong island.

Edgar The wrong island?

Max Simple enough mistake to make—she had the map upside down. And now she's intent on rowing back.

Suzy I am?

Max (*to Edgar*) You see, foolhardy. (*To Suzy*) Yes, it all becomes clear to me now, you are definitely intent on rowing back today, there is no dissuading her. Despite the many dangers.

Edgar Dangers?

Max A sudden squall.

Edgar I don't know, the sea looks quite calm today.

Max Possibly the calm before the storm ... and then what? The boat overturning?—pitching her into the merciless ocean? She could be drowned, Edgar, drowned, her lifeless body swept out to sea ... to be discovered perhaps weeks later. Unrecognizable save for her bright red hair. You have noticed her red hair, Edgar? Of course, it's undeniable ... yes, I'd wager that in her passport it says, "colour of hair—*red* ". If I were you, Miss Stevens—and don't forget Edgar, her name is *Suzy Stevens*, if I were you, I should carry your passport with you always. It could be the only means of identifying you. No matter how soggy it gets.

Edgar She could always wait for the ferry tomorrow.

Max (*throwing up a hand*) No. She is adamant, and quite determined to make that perilous journey. The best I have been able to do is persuade her to leave now.

Suzy What?!

Max *Now*. Before the light fails, and while Edgar is *still here to witness your departure*. All that remains is to see if the coast is clear. (*He strides out on to the patio and stares off, then he returns*) There's no sign of them.

Edgar Them?

Max The cirrus nimbus cloud formation that often heralds a storm. Yes, Miss Stevens. Here is your passport, take it, and make your run to the boat now. (*He hands her a passport from the table*)

Suzy B—But——

Max Those cirrus nimbus are not visible yet, but might be upon us any moment—just go, and stay out of sight of them.

Max urges Suzy to exit through the french doors

> *Suzy exits*

Now, Edgar ...

Edgar You've given me a grand idea for a murder, Max.

Max I'm delighted.

Edgar A drowning, a switch of personality perhaps ... it's all mixed up in my mind at the moment, but it'll come clear to me.

Max (*trying to get Edgar to leave*) Good, good. You should go straight back to your place, lock the door and burn the midnight oil ... and emerge in a few days time—*but certainly no earlier than tomorrow afternoon.*

Edgar That's good advice. I'll do that ... (*He seems about to go—then*) Ah, but I was forgetting ... provisions ... (*he returns to the table*) ... and I replaced some of the ouzo I've drunk here. *And* I brought a little something for Janet ... (*He picks up the orchid*) Where is Janet by the way?

Max She's lying down upstairs.

Edgar I don't wonder—all that rowing.

Max Rowing? Janet? She never goes rowing.

Edgar Eh?

Max No, it's *Suzy Stevens* who goes rowing. You remember Suzy Stevens? The *red-haired* girl?

Edgar But I thought you said——

Max I said—and you agreed—that you should go back to your place and get to work.

Edgar Ay. Ay.

As Max urges him to the french doors

That drowning. I think the motive could be something to do with a will.

Max (*with the faintest hesitation*) Corny, Edgar, corny. You can do better than that—back at your place, *with the drapes drawn against the outside world.*

> *Suzy enters through the french doors*

Suzy I nearly ran into them!

Max What?

Suzy Cirrus nimbus. Coming across the headland. *And hurrying.*

Edgar I'd better go then. I don't want to get caught in the rain.

Max Go? I wouldn't hear of it. You'll disappoint Janet.

Edgar Janet?

Max Yes, if you went to the trouble of buying this, I *insist* that you give it to her personally. (*He thrusts the orchid into Edgar's hands*) Go on, Edgar, the door at the top of the stairs.

Edgar, orchid in hand, starts up the stairs. Max turns to Suzy who is by the french doors

How are the cirrus nimbus?
Suzy Getting closer every minute!

Max looks at Edgar, as he arrives at the bedroom door and hesitates

Max Well, go on Edgar, go on!

Edgar exits into the bedroom

Max starts for the stairs

I'll keep him up there as long as I can. You get rid of them!
Suzy B—But, Max——
Max Look, they think you're my wife, and he knows you're not. Get rid of them!

Max exits into the master bedroom

Suzy remains, and primps her appearance—her hands go to her hair. She realizes that she is not wearing the wig, and turns in a panic. She finds it and puts it on—just in time, as:

George and Mary enter through the french doors

George Phew! That was a climb. I shall be glad to sit down.
Suzy (*blurting*) Max wants to see you urgently.
Mary He does?
Suzy Yes, to your advantage, he said ... something about making a deal.

Mary and George exchange a look

Mary Where is he?
Suzy A—across the headland.
George But we've just come from there.
Suzy Ah, but you took the lower path. (*She urges them back to the french doors*) The upper path—that's where he's waiting for you.
Mary Oh, very well. Come on, George!

George and Mary exit

Suzy relaxes a bit

Now the master bedroom door opens and Max looks out. Suzy gives him the thumbs up

The door closes then opens again—Max looks out

Max The wig!

Suzy jerks the wig off, puts it out of sight

The door opens wider—Max and Edgar enter. Max locks the door and pockets the key

I think Janet enjoyed that little chat. Perked her up.

Edgar But she was asleep the whole time.

As Max and Edgar descend the stairs:

Max Ah, but she smiled I thought—when you gave her the orchid.

Edgar I'm not sure it was a good idea to put it between her hands. When she wakes up, she may think the worst.

Max When she wakes up, it will be a wonderful, wonderful surprise for her. (*To Suzy*) Any change in the weather?

Suzy The cirrus nimbus is moving away towards the headland—on the upper path.

Max Oh, so you'll be off again. *Won't you?*

Suzy Well, I'd hate to waste a good witness to my departure. Good-day, Mr Chambers. Mr Harrington.

Suzy exits through the french doors

Edgar Don't you think one of us should see her off safely?

Max What?

Edgar Shouldn't I at least watch her until she's out of sight.

Max Why on earth would you want to do that?—you hardly know the girl.

Edgar The sudden squall, the merciless sea.

Max If she flounders, it won't be off shore. No, it'll be in the open sea, out of sight around the headland.

Edgar (*moving to exit*) I still think I should go and——

Max Have a drink, Edgar.

Edgar hesitates—Max waves a bottle in front of him

A teeny ouzo? And I think I'll join you. Yes. (*Brooking no argument, he pours a glass while sidling himself between Edgar and the french door. He proffers the glass*) I've never known you refuse a drink.

Edgar (*taking the glass*) If she's got that map upside down again . . .

Max Then she'll row straight back here again and we've nothing to worry about. Cheers.

They drink. Edgar considers

Edgar What drug did you use to knock Janet out?

Max gags on his drink

Oh, come on. I could tell right away she wasn't sleeping naturally. Mind you, understandable after what's probably gone on here today.

Max still stunned, stares at him

There's death in the atmosphere. Don't have to be psychic to know that. Knew as soon as I saw that couple this morning . . . Her in her widow's weeds . . . him with his mourning patch . . . and asking for Janet.

Max (*hoarsely*) Oh, you mean *them!*

Edgar I don't mean to pry, death is a family affair, but they *were* bearers of bad news, weren't they?

Max Yes, a cousin of Janet's died.

Edgar Oh, I'm sorry to hear that, but fortunately she's got you as a husband, Max. Hysterical with grief was she? You had to sedate her?
Max Yes.

Mary and George enter

Edgar Ah, hallo again. I've just heard the sad news.
Mary Sad news?
Edgar Poor Mrs Harrington.
Mary (*eagerly*) She's had a fatal accident?
Edgar The death of her cousin.
Max Her *first* cousin. This, by the way, is her *second* cousin ... Mary Ticklewell, and her husband George. Edgar Chambers.
Edgar How do you do.
George Harrington, we've been looking for you at the end of the path.
Max Whatever for?
Mary *Your wife* (*softer*) ... dear Janet, told us we would find you there.
Max (*realizing*) I see. Well, she was probably confused, upset ...
Edgar It isn't every day you lose a cousin.
Max A *first* cousin. Can I offer you a drink?
George Well ... I ...
Mary Don't you dare, George. You know what drink does to you. You have to keep a clear head ... after all, you have things to discuss with Mr Harrington.
George Things?
Mary *Dealings.*
George Eh? Ah. Oh yes.

George glances at Edgar then leads Max away downstage

Your wife did intimate that you had come to your senses ... and wanted to talk. (*He glances back at Edgar*) Hmm. To talk a deal.
Max A deal! Janet told you that.

Mary comes downstage to join them

Mary She most certainly did.
Max Nothing could be further from my mind. You must have *mis*heard her.
Edgar That's easily done, the way Janet speaks.
Mary What?
Edgar Her lisp.
George } (*together*) Her lisp!
Mary
Max And her Brahms and Beethoven ... She's very fond of music ... *Edgar, what are you still doing here?* You should be at home, working out how to dispose of your murder victims!
Mary What?
Max (*overriding, continuing*) The whole world is waiting, Edgar—for the secret burial of the Wilson family.
Edgar Incineration.

Mary Incineration!?

Max Edgar writes thrillers.

Edgar (*chattily to Mary*) I've decided to burn them, it's so much cleaner.

Max That's very jolly, Edgar, now go and get it down while it's still fresh in your mind.

Edgar (*fired now*) You're right, Max. I'm going.

Max Good.

Edgar (*picking up a bottle of ouzo*) Going back to my place of work . . . I will not be diverted . . . nothing, nothing shall stand between me and my craft.

Edgar exits

Max is relieved

Edgar enters again

Edgar I'm still worried about that girl in the boat.

Max I can see your problem! If she's in a boat on the *water*, it does seem to rule out *incineration* . . . ! (*He starts to hustle Edgar away*)

Edgar But, Max——

Max (*interjecting*) Come on, I'm taking you back to your place, we'll have a drink or two, and sort it all out. (*He turns back to George and Mary*) Make yourselves at home.

Max and Edgar exit

George and Mary regard each other

George Extraordinary, quite extraordinary.

Bemused he unconsciously picks up an ouzo bottle—but before he can pour it—Mary snatches it from him

Mary You have to keep a clear head, George!

George Why?

Mary He may be just playing us along, seeking an advantage.

George He already has that. Yes, my dear, to quote the vernacular, he has us by the short and curlies.

Mary George, don't be vulgar!

George Sorry, dear, but it is the most vivid summation of the facts.

Mary Are you quite sure?

George We both knew it was a forlorn hope coming here. Had he been a simpler sort of chap . . . but, as soon as I saw the cunning flick of his eyes . . . as soon as I saw that face.

Mary grabs his shoulder, and turns him to face her

Mary Would you rather see *this* face?

George quails

   Think of something, George!

George It's hopeless, as first cousin, Janet Harrington is the primary claimant.

Mary And where does that leave me?

George Last. Up the creek without a——
Mary (*interjecting*) I warned you about being vulgar!
George Sorry, dear.
Mary George, I'm *ordering* you to think of something!
George I'm trying.
Mary Think of millions of dollars!
George I do dear, every waking hour.

Mary paces away angrily

Mary We wouldn't have been put in this invidious position if that girl
didn't selfishly want to claim her own inheritance! (*She rounds on George*)
The weak link, George, you're always telling me there's a weak link in
every case!
George Yes, dear, and I'm rather afraid we're it!
Mary (*glowering at him*) No wonder your colleagues say that about you.
George What? What do they say about me? If people are talking about me
behind my back, I've a right to know!
Mary Then I'll say it to your face! You couldn't get a conviction if it was
Jack the Ripper in the dock. Actually doing a murder at the time!
George (*with dignity*) It is documented fact—that the identity of Jack the
Ripper was never . . . (*He stops, reacts*) Documents! *Yes.*
Mary What?
George It may surprise you, but I *have* thought of something. Earlier today,
Harrington intimated that he had in his possession certain documents.
Mary (*interjecting*) Documents. Proof of lineage! (*She starts to rush around,
opening drawers, searching for the documents*) If we can find them and
burn them . . .
George *Examine them*, my dear.
Mary All right, you examine them . . . and I'll burn them!
George To destroy documentary evidence would be tantamount to a
criminal act.
Mary Millions of dollars, George. *Millions!!!*
George I'll take the bureau.

*Mary and George are both searching now. But a fruitless search—they end up
with Mary holding a passport and a policy*

Any luck?
Mary Nothing. Just her passport . . . and an insurance policy . . . (*she
squints at it*) . . . Miserly . . . only ten thousand. (*She turns, and looks up the
stairs*) Of course. Their bedroom. That's where they'd keep them! (*She
puts the passport and the policy on top of the bureau*) Come along, George.

*Mary and George ascend the stairs to the master bedroom. George tries the
door, but it is locked*

Out of the way. (*She pushes George aside and bends to look through the
keyhole. She reacts*) She's in there!
George Who's in there?
Mary A woman, George, a woman.

George I wonder who it is.
Mary George, let me give you a clue. There are only two women on this island, and I am standing here.
George Oh? It's probably Mrs Harrington then.
Mary Probably!? It *is* Mrs Harrington!
George Oh. What's she doing in there?
Mary She's in bed, under the covers and unmoving, so we must presume she's sleeping!
George Oh. Oh, can't disturb her then.

George starts to descend the stairs again. Mary hesitates at the locked door— then she follows him down the stairs. A hopeless pause

Mary (*muttering*) If we could prove she was an imposter or something . . .
George Don't be silly, my dear, that sort of thing happens in books, but never, never in real life.
Mary (*an idea growing*) What if we could prove she was dead?
George Even more ridiculous. The last time I saw her she was far from moribund.
Mary If she *were* to die?
George But, my dear, you've seen her, she appears to be in the most excellent health . . .
Mary *But if she were dead?* Wouldn't that be best for all of us?
George Certainly for you and I. But not for her. Anyway, it's mere conjecture, it isn't going to happen.
Mary It most certainly is.
George Oh dear, how sad, and she seemed in such radiant health.
Mary George, what *are* you talking about?
George Mrs Harrington. Janet. Clearly she has confided to you that her days are numbered.
Mary No, George, I am confiding to *you* that her days are numbered.
George I'm sorry, dear, I don't think I quite understand.
Mary Janet Harrington is going to die.
George That's what I thought you said . . . but you denied——
Mary (*overriding*) She is going to die, because we are going to kill her!
George We?
Mary Well, to be more specific—*you* are going to kill her.
George What?!
Mary Yes, George, it all becomes clear to me now . . . we must do away with her. *You* must.
George You can't be serious?

Mary turns her face at him

Mary Extreme circumstances, George—call for extreme measures . . .
George Yes, but—but . . . murder?!
Mary It has to be quick, George. There must be no unnecessary pain.
George (*faintly*) Thank goodness.
Mary (*overriding*) I insist upon that. Yes, there's too much violence in the world today. It has to be a quick, neat and tidy murder!

George (*interjecting*) Mary, what are you saying!?

Mary stares at George

  Murder?

Mary stares at him

  But . . . how?

Mary For years, George, you have bored me and countless others with beastly tales of your military service, of the snap, crackle and pop of various human bones . . . the crunch of booted feet upon instep. Now is the time, George, to turn all that training to a more practical use.

George But . . . but, Mary . . . we only attacked *sandbags*!

Mary Well, now you can grapple with the real thing. Janet Harrington. I want her dead. I need her dead. And by George, George, *I will have her dead*!

CURTAIN

SCENE 3

The same. Later that night

The stage is shadowy, lit only by moonlight coming through the french doors and windows—and whatever light spills out from the workroom, master and guest bedroom doors as and when they are opened

Mary is at the top of the stairs, on her hands and knees polishing that small area of landing/gallery outside the master bedroom door, and at the top of the stairs. She has put aside the rug to enable her to do this. Her polishing finished, she now replaces the rug, and puts a foot on it and pushes, to demonstrate that it now rests on a slippery surface. She then turns and puts her eye to the keyhole, and satisfied, she turns, almost steps on the rug—but then side-steps it, and hurries down the stairs to put the duster and polish away—then she turns and moves to open the guest room door

Mary Right, George.

No answer

  It's all clear

No answer

  George!

George enters from the guest bedroom, very reluctantly

George I don't want to do it, Mary.

Mary George, I've given you the best years of my life, and now, when I ask you to do one simple, little murder, all you can do is make feeble excuses.

George I don't think I can do it.

Mary Of course you can, you must . . . I haven't slaved away polishing that
landing for nothing. You can do it, and you're going to do it, and now is
the best possible time to do it! *She's* still asleep up there, and *he* isn't back
yet.

George That's the weak link . . . he may come back.

Mary Of course he'll come back, he lives here! But you saw him go off—
you heard him, he and that writer chap are probably in the depths of a
drunken orgy. Anyway, it's part of the plan that he comes back—
eventually—and discovers the body . . . and you, George, seem determined to disappoint him!

George still hesitates

There's no risk as long as you do it now . . . I'll keep a look out. (*She
crosses to the french doors to "look out". A pause—then she becomes aware
that George has not moved*) George!

George I—I think I'd like to reassess our plan.

Mary It couldn't be more simple. You stand here and call her; she awakens;
starts down the stairs and, hopefully, slips on that rug I've been slaving
over—*under*. And then she tragically falls to her death below.

George It isn't much of a fall. She might survive.

Mary It's very likely she *will* survive . . . but not after you get your hands
around her neck, and break it!

George Someone will suspect.

Mary We are going to arrange the scene so that it looks like a perfectly
normal accident.

George still hesitates

George, when we took our vows, you promised to obey.

George Yes, dear . . . (*Suddenly*) No dear, I think that was you.

Mary *Not in my book!* Now do get on with it, George.

George What if we're found out?

Mary Then let's hope we get someone like you handling the prosecution!

*Mary returns to the french doors to keep a look out. Again, George does not
move. She regards him*

George (*looking at her helplessly*) Mary, it's not that I don't love you.

*Mary realizes she has to take the bull by the horns, picking up the bottle of
ouzo, she crosses past George, and towards the guest bedroom*

Mary What you need, George Ticklewell, is some moral courage. Come!

*Mary exits into the guest bedroom, George gratefully exits after her. The
door closes*

*After a slight pause, Max enters, looks around the empty area—then puts
the light on and off in signal, then starts up the stairs. When he gets to the
top, he half slips on the rug*

Max (*muttering*) That's dangerous.

He unlocks the bedroom door and exits into the master bedroom

George enters from the guest bedroom—he crosses to pick up a small glass, then returns to the guest bedroom, he stops half-way, regards the glass, then returns to exchange it for a much larger one. He turns, exits into the guest bedroom again

Suzy enters through the french doors. She is very cold, and shivering. She looks around the area

The master bedroom door opens, Max enters, to remain near the door

Suzy.

Suzy is so cold, she can only make a spasmodic chattering sound

Suzy I'm ... c-c-cold ... b-been w-w-waiting out there for hours for your signal.

Max leans back inside the door, to take a woman's dressing-gown from the back of the door, and he tosses it down to Suzy

Max Here. Put it on, and come on up here, we've got a lot to do, and not much time to do it in.

Suzy starts to pull on the robe—then pauses

Suzy (*reacting*) A l-l-lot to do?
Max We've still got to dye your hair—dye hers ... and then get her into the boat.
Suzy We're still going ahead with it then?
Max Of course we're going on with it. Everything's working perfectly.
Suzy What about Edgar?
Max Edgar's a key witness. He saw you going off to row to your death.
Suzy I didn't mean that. *They* ... (*she points down at the guest bedroom*) ... think I'm Janet ... and when Edgar turns up here tomorrow——
Max (*interjecting*) If Edgar turns up at all, it will be very late tomorrow—I laced him with enough ouzo to put him out for hours ... and by that time, they will have gone back on the ferry—and us along with them, to contact your lawyer. Now come on up and help me.

Suzy hurries up the stairs to Max. When she gets to the top she slips on the rug. He grabs her and holds her

That *is* dangerous. (*He pushes the rug to one side with his foot—then smiles at her*) My goodness, if I were to lose you now, what would I do!?

Max and Suzy exit into the master bedroom

George enters from the guest bedroom—he moves out, holding glass in hand—drains it—and looks up the stairs—he seems about to call but then abruptly turns, glass in hand, and exits into the guest bedroom again

Suzy enters from the master bedroom, to hurry down the stairs to the kitchen area, to pick up the bowl—she hurries up the stairs again—and even as she starts to exit into the master bedroom, George enters from the guest bedroom—Mary enters behind him, pushing him out. George is starting to behave a bit drunkenly now

George But I'm not ready yet.

Mary If you get any more ready, you won't be able to stand up.

George Just one more. Moral courage.

Mary George, you're awash with moral courage. Are you going to do it, or aren't you?

George Aren't. (*Swaying a fraction now—but with a new-found courage growing*) Not yet. You see, my dear . . . no, I'll brook no argument, there is one thing we have both overlooked.

Mary What's that?

George That unhappy heiress up there is soon to depart this life. We must . . .

Mary Must what?

George Drink her health first! It's the only decent thing.

And in one lunging plunge, George exits into the guest bedroom again. Mary hesitates, then has no alternative, but to exit after him. The door closes

The master bedroom door opens—Max and Suzy enter, carrying Janet's unconscious body between them. Both Suzy and Janet wear hair-enveloping bath-hats. Max and Suzy descend to the main floor area and move towards the french doors

Max Just help me to the top of the path, I can manage her from there . . . then you come back here, and clean up in the bedroom.

Max and Suzy exit with Janet

A long pause then the guest bedroom door opens, George enters, then Mary enters. George is not so much drunk, as feeling the effects of a lot of liquor consumed quickly. George starts straight up the stairs

Mary Where do you think you are going?

George I'm ready, and I want to get it over with as quickly as possible.

Mary You do it *down here*, George. I'm not letting you go alone into another woman's bedroom!

George But I'm only going to kill her.

Mary *Come down here*, George.

George descends again

And compose yourself.

George It's difficult. I still don't want to do it . . . (*Quickly before she can protest*) But I know I have to. I'm resigned to that now.

Mary Very well then—call her.

George I hope she does slip on the rug—then I won't have to . . . Oh dear.

Mary We won't know if she's going to slip until you call her.

George Yes, dear.

Mary Go on then!

George braces himself

George (*whispering*) Janet.
Mary Louder, George.
George It seems so uncharitable to awaken someone at this time of night . . . and then kill them . . .
Mary (*calling*) Janet!

George reacts—the deed must be done now

    Janet!

There is a pause

George (*hopefully*) She isn't there.
Mary Of course she's there. (*She calls*) JANET!
Suzy (*off*) Yes?

A stunned moment for Mary and George—and then, as one, they turn to the french doors

    Suzy enters through the french doors, still wearing the robe and bath-hat

George By Jove!
Mary (*still confused*) Janet! My dear. We . . . we thought you were in bed.
Suzy I was. But I couldn't sleep . . . decided to take a stroll . . . what did you want?
George Want?
Suzy I thought I heard you calling me.
George Oh . . . er . . . oh, well, yes, as a matter of fact you did, but . . . nothing urgent . . . it can wait until tomorrow.

He speaks at Mary, who has not moved—who is very still

    Can't it, dear?

Mary does not answer

    (*Covering now*) Yes, I'm sure it can.

Suzy regards them uncertainly for a moment

Suzy (*heading for the stairs*) Well, good-night then.

Suzy is about to ascend the stairs when Mary suddenly moves at last and on impulse snatches up one of the identical vases which she shatters across the back of Suzy's head. Suzy falls unconscious

There is a chilly silence—a moment of stillness as both George and Mary regard Suzy, realizing they are committed now. Finally, Mary breaks the moment, and moves to look at Suzy

Mary She's still breathing, you must finish her off. There's no going back now, George.

He does not move

(With a rising note of hysteria in her voice) George.

He moves at last and regards the body. Then he bends over it hands outstretched, then suddenly he straightens up

George Help me get her into the chair.
Mary I don't think I can bring myself to touch her.

George, committed now, and the legal man in him taking over—the latent authority

George *(overriding)* I need her upright. *Help me!*

Mary responds to his command, and together they lift Suzy into a chair, and prop her into a sitting position. George puts his hands on her neck, and then, without releasing the hold, moves around the chair until he is behind her—and then slightly changes his position and hold so that it becomes a wrestler's neck-breaking hold. He applies the first pressure—Mary stands transfixed with horror

Replace the vase with that one at the top of the stairs. The pieces down here . . . it'll look as though she knocked it over when she fell. Hurry!

As George applies more pressure on Suzy's neck. Mary runs up the stairs to pick up the vase

Don't forget the rug! That fell too.

Mary pauses, then puts her foot on the rug and pushes it off the gallery. She starts down the stairs again and is almost at the bottom when there is a loud crack. Mary and George both freeze, then after a moment George straightens up and lets Suzy's body loll in the chair

(He turns to meet Mary's eyes) It's done.
Mary Are you sure?!
George You heard it, didn't you! *(He regards Suzy's body, then drags it off the chair and on to the floor)* Now all we do is place her under the stairs. *(He does so)*

They regard each other, then suddenly George's momentary determination totally deserts him, he even looks limp

I think I'm going to be sick.

George suddenly rushes across to exit into the guest bedroom

Mary pauses to regard Suzy then she too hurries over to exit into the guest bedroom. The door closes

There is a pause

Max enters through the french doors. He does not see the body as he hurries up the stairs. He reaches the master bedroom, and, as he opens the door:

Max Darling, it's over . . . a couple of minutes from now the boat should be flooded and . . . *(He stops)* Suzy?

Max exits fully into the master bedroom

(*Off*) Suzy?

Max enters from the master bedroom again, frowning

Suzy? Where are you, darling . . . ? (*A sudden thought*) Ah—the workroom . . . (*He hurries down the stairs—turns towards the workroom—and stumbles over Suzy's body*) Suzy? (*He crouches and briefly examines her*) Suzy? (*He touches the rug nearby*) That damned rug! (*The shock hits him, then realization. He stands up and then another shocking thought hits him. He stops dead, and glances at his watch*) "A couple of minutes and the boat'll be flooded"! (*He rushes to the french doors*) Janet!

Max exits through the french doors, leaving Suzy's body on stage

The CURTAIN *falls*

ACT II

Scene 1

The farmhouse interior. The next morning

It is, as usual, a bright sunny morning. Nothing has changed save that the rug is back at the top of the stairs and Suzy's body has gone!

The guest bedroom door opens and Mary and George appear. George is nursing a bit of a headache. They remain near the door, and so are screened from seeing under the lee of the stairs where the body should be

Mary Obviously he got back so drunk last night, he didn't notice—or hasn't returned at all yet.

George It means *we* will have to discover the body.

Mary But, George, it would have so much more impact if *he* does the discovering. Must we?

George Imperative. We must continue to act normally ... and normality dictates that we would be up at this hour and preparing to catch the ferry.

Mary Very well then. How do you think we should go about it?

George Well, I will stroll *nonchalantly* towards the patio, while you, *casually*, set about making a cup of tea. Then you *idly* glance in the general direction of the body ... scream, thereby drawing *my* attention ... whereupon *I*——

Mary (*interjecting*) Oh, come on, George, let's get on with it!

George, ultra nonchalant, strolls out towards the french doors. Mary strolls towards the table. She reaches it, glances to where the body should be and screams

George (*spinning round*) Oh, very well done, dear! (*Then he reacts to find the body gone*) But there is no body.

Mary No.

George Why did you scream then!?

Mary Where's it gone, where's it gone?

George It's been stolen.

Mary (*momentarily diverted*) But they haven't taken the radio or the silver or ... (*She rounds on him*) What do you mean, it's been stolen!? People don't go around stealing bodies.

George Burke and Hare did.

Mary She was lying right there! Dead! *George, you obviously bungled it!*

George You were there. You saw me. You heard her neck crack ... Oh, dear.

Mary What?

George I have heard of cases ... people with a broken neck ... they can survive for a while.

Mary For how long?

George I don't know—long enough perhaps for her to have dragged herself to the doors ... (*he moves to the french doors*) ... and crawl away somewhere, like some wounded animal—to die.

Mary Yes—and then her husband came back, saw the broken vase and the rug on the floor ...

George Probably thought the rug had fallen and toppled the vase ...

Mary So he cleared up—went to bed, none the wiser ...

The master bedroom door opens and Max enters—and comes cheerily down the stairs

Max Morning. You're up early.

Mary We—we, don't want to miss the ferry.

Max (*pouring a glass of orange juice and starting back up the stairs*) Oh, no rush, stay another day if you want ... I know Janet would be pleased. Anyway, we can all talk about it at breakfast.

Max exits into the master bedroom

Mary and George regard each other

Mary If he came back, and tidied up ... surely he'd notice his wife was missing from the nuptial bed?

George We don't know *when* he came back—could have been as you said a drunken orgy with that writer chap ... He probably only got back a little while ago ...

Mary Found the bed empty and thought that his wife was off walking around the headland.

George And actually she's lying out there somewhere. Her neck broken.

Mary What are we going to do, George?

George Eh?

Mary She is supposed to be lying dead *there*—under the stairs. Instead she's outside somewhere ... How could she break her neck out there?

George Goats.

Mary Goats?

George (*firmly*) Goats. There are goats on this island somewhere. *Wild* goats. Yes, that's it, she was trampled to death by wild goats.

Mary *George*. George, I was about to say that is the most ridiculous thing I have ever heard in my life. But it's all we've got, so we'd better stick with it.

George Rely on me, dear.

Mary (*eyes to heaven*) God preserve us!

Mary paces away and then rounds on him

Mary Suppose she isn't dead? Suppose she comes crawling back into this room—her head all to one side!

George Well ... well, we'll have to convince her it was just a joke, that's all.

Mary Suddenly the goats sound quite feasible!

The master bedroom door opens—Max enters and comes down the stairs, then busies himself laying up a breakfast table

Max Made up your minds yet? Whether you're leaving or staying?
George We are certainly staying until the stampede subsides.
Max Stampede?
George (*off on his story*) Of goats. *Wild* goats. Surely you heard the thunder of their vicious hooves just now? Look, there goes another one!

Max spins round to stare at the empty french doors

Max Goats?
George The island's overrun with them. I just hope that some innocent person doesn't get trampled to death out there—*their neck broken*. I'm rather concerned about your wife.
Max Janet?
George Yes, out there alone, walking the headland and . . .
Max No, no, she's up there in bed.

Mary and George react. They turn to gaze up the stairs and at this moment:

The master bedroom door opens and Janet enters, her hair is now bright red

Ah, darling, just talking about you.
Janet Good-morning. (*She comes down the stairs, smiling brightly*) Good-morning, George . . . Mary . . . hope you slept well?

George and Mary are totally stunned

I think I owe you both an apology, I wasn't really myself yesterday—the shock of dear cousin Jonathan's death you know . . . now what's this about you leaving? I wouldn't hear of it, after all, we've hardly got to know each other. Although Mary and I have met before, haven't we.
Mary (*hoarsely*) Have we?
Janet Of course. Oh, I don't really expect you to remember. I was just a child at the time. At Great Aunt Jessica's funeral.
Mary (*finally*) You're not the same person.
Max Well, so long ago; there's bound to be some change.
George Your hair!
Janet Oh, I *see*! That's what's been bothering you. Yes, I dyed it, last night . . . I'm a creature of sudden impulse . . . and I thought, as an heiress who's soon to inherit a fortune I'd change my whole personality.
Max Come along, darling, time for our jog.
Janet Our *jog*? But, Max, you know we don't jog——
Max (*interjecting*) Don't want you going the same way as dear cousin Jonathan, do we? . . . Got to keep you fit . . . keep you alive and well.

Janet and Max exit, jogging off through the french doors

There is a slight pause

George Mary, I know I can be a bit slow on the uptake, and I don't want to press the point . . . but I could be almost positive that the woman who has just left this room is *not* the same woman I murdered last night ... and I honestly don't think I could forget a thing like that.

Mary George!

George (*quickly*) Yes, dear ... you're right, it *was* the same woman.

Mary Of course it wasn't the same woman!

George Thank goodness, and I thought it was the ouzo. Well, that's that then.

Mary That's what?!

George The mystery's solved. It wasn't the ouzo.

Mary George, that woman is *not* Janet Harrington.

George Yes, it's clear to me now.

Mary What is?

George (*faltering*) It's clear to me, that nothing is clear to me.

Mary George, we murdered the real Janet Harrington last night. You did it.

George Thank goodness, I thought it might all have just been a terrible dream!

Mary Obviously he *did* come back, find the body—and what was his immediate conclusion?

George She'd been trampled to death by goats?

Mary That she'd had an accident! Fell down the stairs—broke her neck! Our plan worked, George. It worked!

George Oh, can we go home now then?

Mary George, we can *not* go home—don't you see? We killed his wife and he's hidden the body and found another one.

George Well, he's probably got a way with women.

Mary *George*. The wife he has now is *not* his wife.

George Ah!

Mary We are back in charge of the situation, George.

George Yes, I'm beginning to get your drift—we can nail him for bigamy!

Mary George! If the wife he has now is not his wife, then what is she?

George An imposter?

Mary Ah, I'm finally getting through to you, George.

George And if we can *prove* the impostor is an impostor.

Mary We've got them by the short and curlies.

George *Mary!*

Mary I don't care, George. They've completely lost my respect. Anyone who could wilfully move *our* body—after we went to so much trouble—is capable of anything. (*Happily now*) She is an impostor—and we are home and dry.

George Not quite, dear. The weak link.

Mary What weak link?

George It's a question of how we put it. I mean, if we say, that is not the girl we murdered last night ... you never know, it might open up a line of enquiry which might be detrimental to our claim. Besides which, at this moment, we can't *prove* that other woman is not his wife.

Mary What!?

George If he's gone this far, he must have some means of backing it up.

Mary Well, what *do* we do?

George If we could produce an independent witness . . .

Edgar enters through the french doors

Mary and George turn to regard him. Their prayers have been answered!
Edgar has a terrible hangover

Edgar Oh, morning. Max around?
Mary He's out jogging.
Edgar Jogging? It's not like Max to indulge in exercise.
Mary I don't suppose it's his wife's cup of tea either?
Edgar Janet? Oh, no, she's quite athletic. Does a lot of rowing . . . (*He frowns*) I think.
Mary Oh, you know Mrs Harrington quite well then, do you?
Edgar Been neighbours for three years . . . I really came over for the hair of the dog—we drank my place dry last night. Max won't mind if I help myself . . . You haven't seen an ouzo bottle lying around, have you?
Mary There's one in our bedroom. Fetch it, George.

George exits into the guest bedroom

If you've been neighbours for three years, you must know Mrs Harrington *awfully* well.
Edgar Yes.
Mary By sight, in fact.

George enters from the guest bedroom, carrying an ouzo bottle, with very little in it

Edgar Yes.
Mary So if she came jogging into this room now—you'd recognize her straight away.
Edgar I dunno. Not sure I'd recognize my own reflection this morning . . . (*He takes the bottle from George*) Mind you, once I've driven some of this inside me. (*He drinks, wipes his mouth—and, a bit brighter now*) That's better. Tell Max I won't see him for a day or two—determined to get on with the book.

Edgar is about to leave—but Mary intercedes

Mary Oh, but you can't leave now, can he, George?
George No. (*Frowning*) Why not?
Mary The independent witness, George.
George Ah.
Edgar What?
Mary Oh, a case we were discussing before you arrived.
Edgar Case?
Mary Yes, yes, my husband is a lawyer you know, and he——
Edgar A lawyer!? Criminal or civil!?
George Well . . . er . . . I——
Mary (*interjecting*) Criminal. Oh, the murder trials he's attended!

Edgar
George } (*together*) Murder?

Mary Yes, George ... I am sure that Mr Chambers ... *being a thriller writer*, might benefit from a chat with you ... at least until the Harringtons get back.

George Oh, yes. I see. Yes, Mr Chambers, I *have* been involved in murder.

Edgar Recently?

George It seems like only yesterday.

Edgar Where did it happen?

George Oh, far from here. Yes, definitely far from here. In the ... er ... in the ... (*He looks out of the french doors*) In the Gobi Desert.

Edgar The desert? Mmmm ... that's an interesting locale ... What method was used?

George Goats.

Edgar Goats?!

George (*firmly*) Goats. Wild ones.

Edgar I see—and they butted the victim to death, did they?

George (*reacting*) Yes. Of course! Butted ... (*At Mary*) That's *much* more sensible than trampling—I mean, goats *do* butt, don't they? Thank you, Mr Chambers.

Mary is looking out through the french doors

Mary (*smugly*) The Harringtons are returning, and I think *someone* is in for a big shock!

Max enters, jogging, panting a bit

Max Edgar! Didn't expect to see you up and about so early.

Mary I bet you didn't!

Edgar Came to borrow some booze—glad I did—you didn't tell me he was a lawyer—been giving me some tips on murder and goats.

Max Haven't seen one all morning.

Edgar What?

Max A murder. Or a goat.

George and Mary are intent on the french doors—reacting now as:

Janet jogs in

Edgar (*staring at her*) Oho, and who is this then? Come on, Max, aren't you going to introduce me?

Mary (*triumphantly*) Yes, Mr Harrington. Go ahead and introduce her!

Janet Oh, come on Edgar—do you like it or don't you?

Edgar smiles, and briefly embraces Janet and kisses her cheek

Edgar Janet. Whatever colour you may dye your hair ... you'll always be the same, lovable you.

Mary reacts as though hit by an invisible fist, her legs shake, and she has to clutch a chair for support

Janet I didn't get a chance to thank you for the wonderful orchid.

Edgar It was nothing—compared with what you've done for me over the past few years—you and Max. But I've got to be going . . . (*He turns to George and Mary*) Thank you for the——(*He reacts to Mary*) Is your wife all right?

George I think she's had a bit of a shock. Come along, my dear . . . I think you should lie down for a while.

They move towards the guest bedroom

I might join you.

George and Mary exit into the guest bedroom. The door closes on them

Edgar, Max and Janet gaze after them

Edgar She must be clairvoyant.

Max Who?

Edgar Her—Mrs Ticklewell—just a few moments ago—before you came in, she predicted that *someone* was in for a big shock. Amazing. Well, I'll see you . . .

Edgar exits

Finally Max and Janet are alone—and now she suddenly flops with sheer exhaustion

Janet Phew!

Max I'm proud of you, darling. You were magnificent.

Janet Really? Did I do well?

Max You did exactly as I wanted you to do.

Janet I'm still very confused. (*She looks up the stairs*) I slipped and fell down the stairs . . . ?

Max And passed out completely. I can tell you, darling, I was desperately worried.

Janet But, what was seaweed doing at the top of the stairs?

Max Seaweed!?

Janet Didn't you tell me I slipped on some seaweed?

Max Whatever gave you such an idea? Seaweed!? The rug, darling, you slipped on the rug.

Janet Then you carried me up to the bedroom?

Max What else could I do? There's no phone here, and the ferry had gone. Anyway, you were breathing normally . . . and then, thank goodness, you slept very peacefully.

Janet Yes, that's one thing I *do* remember . . . sleeping for a long, long time.

Max Not that long. About an hour or so. Then you got up, and seemed fully recovered.

Janet Then—they . . . George and Mary Ticklewell . . . arrived?

Max That's right—and they told you about your cousin's death, and the will.

Janet That's funny. I could swear I never met them until this morning.

Max (*laughing*) Well, my darling, you *did* meet them, and you'll just have to take my word for it.

Janet Then what happened?

Max I can only assume you were suffering from delayed concussion ... perhaps that, together with the shock of the news ... anyway, soon as you started behaving irrationally ... dashing off to dye your hair ... that's when I knew I had to adopt this plan ...

Janet Plan?

Max Yes, darling ... a cover-up plan.

Janet That's the thing I still don't really understand. Why, Max ... what are you covering up?

Max I'm doing it for you, darling. They're a couple of opportunists, and they're desperate ... I knew that if they saw even a hint of unusual behaviour they'd bring an insanity suit.

Janet I'm not insane.

Max Of course you're not, but yesterday you were like someone under the influence of drugs. I had to protect you.

Janet Max, you take such good care of me.

Max You're worth it.

They kiss lightly

Janet Cornflakes.

Max Eh?!

Janet (*rising and moving to the table*) I—I was sitting here and—and ... suddenly a plate of cornflakes came up and hit me? (*She looks querulously at Max*) Oh, Max, I'm not going mad, am I?

Max No, darling—at very worst, a temporary amnesia.

Janet Yes. I suppose it may all come back to me sometime.

Max I shouldn't push it, darling. Now, come on, I'm going to put you to bed for a while.

Max starts to lead her towards the stairs

Janet I hope I don't have those dreams again.

Max What dreams?

Janet It's all mixed up ... I'm locked in that room up there.

Max That's no dream—I *did* lock you in.

Janet Why?

Max I didn't want you falling down the stairs again.

Janet And what about the rowing?

Max Rowing?

Janet I was in a boat, Max and the water was flooding in and——

Max That *was* a dream. You don't think I'd let you go out rowing on your own, do you? No, darling, you are far too precious to me.

They reach the bedroom door—then Janet stops

Janet I saw *her* too.

Max Saw who?

Janet Suzy Stevens. She was in my dream, and yet it wasn't her ... her hair was different——

Max (*interjecting*) My darling! I promise you—neither you nor I will ever see Suzy Stevens again.

Max and Janet exit into the master bedroom

A pause. Then George enters from the guest bedroom

George I'm sure I saw a spare towel out here. Ah, yes! (*He crosses to the sink—takes a towel—soaks it, wrings it out, when he happens to see the passport lying where Mary left it. On impulse, he picks it up—opens it— frowns, puts it down—moves back to the guest bedroom. Then stops profoundly. He hurries back to pick up the passport again—studies it carefully, his excitement mounting*)

Mary (*off*) George! Have you got it, George?

George Yes, dear, I rather think I have.

Mary enters from the guest bedroom, and remains in the doorway, holding her head

Mary Well, bring it here then.

George crosses to her, holding the passport

George, I have a crashing headache, and if you think I'm going to apply a *passport* to my brow . . .

George No, dear—*look*.

He opens the passport—she looks at it—he points out something

Here. Look at that. See . . . here?

Mary (*staring*) George, I never ever thought I would say this . . . but I am almost proud of you.

George We've got them, dear . . . we've got them by . . . well, you know what we've got them by.

Mary We have. *We have!* And now we'll turn the screw.

George I think you're mixing your metaphors, dear, but I know what you mean.

George hurries over to the bureau to look for, and finds, a sheet of paper—he sits down, and starts to write rapidly

Mary (*moving nearer*) What are you doing?

George The thing I know how to do best. Call him, dear.

Mary Now?

George While the iron's hot.

Mary (*calling*) Mr Harrington. Mr Harrington!

The master bedroom door opens and Max enters

Max Shh . . . you'll wake my wife.

Mary Come now, I didn't call loud enough to wake the dead!

Max What?

Mary Please come down here, Mr Harrington, there is something we wish to discuss with you.

Max Look, can't it wait until ——?
Mary (*interjecting*) This concerns millions of dollars. And it can't wait
another moment. Down here if you please.

Max hesitates, then closes the bedroom door—descends to George and Mary

Max Well?
Mary We know what you're up to, Mr Harrington.
Max Up to?
George That woman up there is *not* Janet Harrington. She's an impostor.
Max Oh, come on ...
Mary She is *not* your wife.

Max regards them

Max (*finally*) Oh, I *see*. This is a last, desperate attempt to get in on cousin
Jonathan's will.
George I reiterate, that woman up there is an impostor.
Max Sorry, but it isn't going to work.

They regard him

Look, I'd know my own wife, wouldn't I ... ? And even if I didn't, there
are witnesses ... documents——
George (*interjecting*) Witnesses—like that writer fellow you bribed to
perjure himself!? Documents ... ? Like this!?

George produces the passport—and opens it at Max

Max (*staring at it*) Janet's passport!
George Oh, that is what it *says*, "Janet Harrington" ... but look closely.

Max does so

I draw your attention in particular to the photograph ...
Max Photograph? Well, you know what these passport photos are ... !?
George I am not referring to the likeness itself, but to the fact that ... on
close scrutiny, it is quite obvious that this passport has been tampered
with ... this photograph has been substituted!

Max stares at the passport

Now what *honest* reason could anyone have for doing that?

Max, for the first time, is at a loss for words

You seem to be at a loss for words, Mr Harrington? Can you offer no
explanation? I think I can. Last night, in this very room, your wife ...
Mary Your *real* wife ...
George Lay dead beneath these stairs ...
Mary Obviously the result of a tragic accident ...
George We found her body, Mr Harrington ...
Mary And we immediately set off to find you.
George Did we?
Mary Yes, George, immediately—but unfortunately we got lost.

George Really? Not easy to do on an island this small ...

Mary *We got lost* and stumbled our way through the darkness ... *Didn't we, George?!—stumbled—*oblivious to ... to the dangers of ... of wild goats!

George Goats *butt*, you know ... many people mistakenly think they *trample* ... but, oh, no—*they butt*!

Mary *George*! We wandered across the island and eventually came full circle ... back here ... to find that the body was gone. *Wasn't it, George?*

George Oh, quite definitely. And then, when *you* returned——

Mary (*interjecting*) And introduced a complete stranger as your wife ...

George That was when we suspected that all was not as it seemed. But the fortuitous discovery of this passport, has solved everything.

Mary Particularly for us. I am now the only surviving claimant, *indisputably*!

Max (*at last*) All this ... over a passport ... ?!

George If you wish, Mr Harrington, we could submit this passport to the proper authorities ... But I warn you, they will carry out forensic tests, and then the truth ... *the whole truth* ... will out.

Max (*after regarding them for a moment*) What do you want?

George and Mary relax and smile

George Ah. Just sign this paper. (*He offers Max paper and pen*)

Max (*hesitating*) What is it?

George A full admission of your duplicity. Now sign—or face the consequences of a full inquiry.

Max, beaten at last, regards him—then grabs paper and pen, signs and tosses it down on the table. George picks it up, scans it and he carefully pockets the paper. He pats his pocket

Now that I have this—I am sure that neither you ... nor that woman up there, whoever she is, will be pursuing any further claims.

Mary throws her arms around him, and kisses him on the cheek

Mary George, you were wonderful!

George Yes, dear, I rather think I was ... What next? Shall we both take a gentle stroll around the island ... ? Who knows, you may even be tempted into buying it ... or do you prefer the south of France ... ?

George and Mary exit

Max is alone—stunned into immobility for a moment—and then he grabs up the passport—looks at it—then viciously tosses it away

Max Damn! (*He paces away*) Damn, damn, damn! And I was so close ... so close I could almost count it! Damn! (*He goes to the french doors*) And damn you too!

Then, as he turns away from one side of the french doors, hands grab at Max's shoulder making him almost jump out of his skin. He yells, turns, reacts and sees:

Suzy. She is exhausted, muddy and damp. And she still wears the bath-hat

Suzy!

She stumbles against him so hard, that he retreats, supporting her, to the sofa—and begins to recover a bit

Suzy, you're alive!?

Suzy And I'm cold and wet again and my neck hurts . . . and . . . (*she pulls off the bath-hat to reveal blonde hair*) . . . my hair's all blonde and . . . *Oh, Max*! (*Weeping, she falls against him*)

Max What happened?

Suzy I don't know. I'm not sure, it's all like a terrible nightmare. I remember rowing. Yes, I was in a boat, and it was sinking . . . and water flooding in through the bunghole . . . that's what must have woke me up. And . . . then I was swimming . . . And then I must have passed out again. I woke up on the beach . . . cold . . . and my neck hurts, and my head hurts and . . . *Janet*! (*Sudden realization*) We were going to drown Janet. Where is Janet?

Max Bed.

Suzy What?

Max The ocean bed.

Suzy Oh. We did it then? Yes . . . I helped you carry her out from here and——

Max (*interjecting*) Then you disappeared. I came back here, and you'd gone. I was distraught, my darling . . . I thought you might have been . . . been trampled to death by goats! I scoured the whole island, and then——

Suzy (*interjecting*) I *did* come back here. (*She turns to stare at the guest bedroom*) And they were calling me . . . they were calling "Janet Harrington". And then . . . then . . . *she* hit me . . . with a vase!

Max *She* hit you!?

Suzy Mary Ticklewell!—then I don't remember anymore until . . . *He* was behind me . . . his hands around my neck . . . and I couldn't shout or move . . . and then there was a terrible crack . . .

Max Your neck?

Suzy No. I think it must have been his watch chain. (*She opens her hand and proffers a watch fob*) I woke up with this in my hand.

Max stares at it

Well, it's a fob of some kind, isn't it? Off a watch chain . . .

Max And there are initials on it—"G.T." (*Then, triumph, and an idea growing*) "G.T." George Ticklewell. So it wasn't an accident.

Suzy Max, *they tried to murder me!*

Max Wonderful.

Suzy What?

Max That you survived.

At this moment there is a clatter from the master bedroom. Max spins round to stare up there

Suzy Max? You're not going to let them get away with it, are you?!
Max (*thinking fast*) No, I'm going to make them pay.
Suzy How? (*Then*) It will mean a change of plan, won't it?
Max (*his mind made up*) A slight change—yes.
Suzy How?
Max Show me that fob again.

Suzy extends it to him

You hold on to that tightly, it's vital evidence.
Suzy But what are you going to do?
Max (*overriding*) He was behind you, you say?
Suzy Yes.
Max (*moving behind her*) Like this?
Suzy Yes.
Max And his hands were ... so?
Suzy Yes.
Max And you felt them tighten ... ?
Suzy (*strangled*) Yes ...

Max begins to strangle her

Max I'm sorry, my darling, I really am ... and I *did* love you ... but you
have to understand ... we're talking about millions of dollars ...
millions!

*Suzy is struggling now, but Max keeps his hold and now drags Suzy back
and into the workroom. We hear faint sounds of a struggle, then silence*

*A pause—then Max enters from the workroom holding the sugar bowl—he
closes the door behind him and composes himself. Then quickly he moves to
produce a soft drink, and pours it into a glass. He adds a quantity of the
"sugar" from the bowl—and then turns towards the stairs holding the glass.
Max ascends the stairs—and, just as he stands outside the bedroom door—it
opens and Janet appears*

Darling, I looked up "concussion" in our medical book, and the
treatment is ... lots of fluids ... and lots of rest.

*Max, holding the glass, urges Janet back into the bedroom—they exit into
it, the door closes*

A pause, then Max enters from the bedroom again

Don't forget, drink it all down ... and then lots of rest, eh?

*Max closes the door, and then hurries down the stairs, exits into the
workroom. A beat then Max enters again, dragging Suzy's body with him.
She is quite dead this time!*

*Max takes her, and places her exactly as she was before. He steps back and
adjusts her position. Then, satisfied, he crosses to pick up the waste-bin from
the kitchen area—he moves back to dump broken pieces of vase where they*

once were. He replaces the waste-bin—again regards the scene—then remembers something. He runs up the stairs—gets to the top, and puts his foot on the rug. He pushes it off the gallery. This done, he looks at the master bedroom door then hurries to do what he has forgotten—lock the door. This done, he again relaxes and remains on the gallery. There is a pause

Mary (*off*) You must have lost it in the house somewhere.
George (*off*) I hope so, my father gave me that watch fob . . .

Mary and George enter through the french doors. George pauses to fumble at his broken watch chain—Mary pauses too

Mary George, we can now afford a *thousand* watch fobs!
George Yes, but that particular one means so much.
Mary All right, George, we'll have a look for it . . .

Mary and George cross into the room, she turns towards the body—he the other way. Suddenly Mary sees Suzy's body—and screams

George Oh good you've found it! (*He turns and sees the body too. He takes it in, then, steps closer. Finally*) She must have crawled right round the island and back again.
Mary It's not the same woman.
George Oh, really, Mary, don't start *that* again.
Mary But her hair's blonde.
George White with shock. Perhaps she crawled into a herd of wild goats!
Mary George, she's dead.
George I *know* she's dead, dear. After all, I killed her!
Max (*from the gallery*) I would say that qualifies as a confession.

Max starts to confidently come down the stairs. They react

Mary George, don't say anything until you've seen a lawyer.
George I *am* a lawyer, dear.
Mary Well, do something!
Max Not much to do, I'm afraid. That's right, isn't it George? You being a lawyer and all, you'd know when to settle? (*He faces up to them*) Let me give you the full picture. *She* lies dead—and clutched in her hand is a watch fob. A watch fob bearing the initials "G.T."
Mary George, how could you be so careless!? It's criminal!
Max Yes, I suppose I *should* make sure it gets into the hands of the proper authorities—but where's the profit in that? The truth coming out? The whole truth? That isn't going to do either of us any good, is it? And, after all, millions of dollars makes for an awfully big pie . . .
George (*eagerly*) A deal?
Mary Fifty-fifty?
Max Reluctantly, yes. Fifty-fifty.
George ⎱ (*together*) Agreed.
Mary ⎰

Max bends to take the fob from Suzy's hand

Max And you get your fob back.

George eagerly reaches for it, but Max withdraws and pointedly "hmmhmms".
George, understanding, pulls out the paper Max signed—and, as one, they
hand over paper and fob

George I can't tell you how relieved I am, to reach such a *civilized*
  conclusion. At least one feels one is dealing with a gentleman.
Max If I'm not—Chiddingbury has a lot to answer for.
George Chiddingbury!? You didn't go to Chiddingbury too!?
Max You mean *you*!? When?
George Forty-nine. You?
Max Fifty-six.
George Good Lord, you must have known Doctor Potterton then?
Max Old Potty? A straight bat and a hard cane—thwack!
George Good Lord. D'you hear that, Mary . . . ? Harrington . . . *Max* here
  . . . he was at Chiddingbury——
Mary (*interjecting*) Yes, I heard, and I'm sure you'll both have lots to talk
  about—*after* we get back to the business in hand.

George and Max come back to earth as they join Mary in regarding Suzy's
body

Max Shouldn't take long—there are two more rowing boats down in the
  bay.
George Consign her to the depths?
Max Yes.
George Righty ho. (*He moves as though to lift the body—then pauses to look*
  up the stairs) What about that woman up there posing as your wife?
  Suppose she comes down unexpectedly and . . .
Max No chance of that. (*He lifts the sugar bowl*) I gave her a spoonful of
  this—concoction of my own—she'll sleep for a while yet.
George Good thinking. But then—wouldn't expect anything else of you
  . . . (*To Mary*) If I'd known from the outset that he had been to
  Chiddingbury . . .
Mary Well, it's all worked out for the best.
Max Come on.

George and Max move to pick up Suzy—then Max pauses, looks at Mary

  She has to help too.
Mary Me?
Max Then we are all implicated—accomplices—a team, eh, George . . . up
  school—and all that.
George He's right, my dear. Up school—*up*!

All three lift Suzy's body

  You know, I do wish we had met under slightly happier circumstances . . .
Mary What could be happier than millions of dollars even if it is a fifty-fifty
  split?
Max Exactly. And when we get back from this last little chore, we'll drink
  to it, eh?

George Jolly good idea.

Max I've got a decanter of rare old Napoleon brandy set aside for an occasion like this . . .

Max, George and Mary exit through the french doors, carrying Suzy's body

A pause—then suddenly we hear the locked master bedroom door rattle

Janet (*off*) Max? MAX!

CURTAIN

SCENE 2

The same. A few minutes later

The stage is empty, the rug still lies where it fell, and the broken pieces of vase still litter the floor

Then, off stage, we hear Max starting to whistle, "Hi-ho-hi-ho, it's home from work we go." Then, off stage, George takes up the tune too—then Mary, off stage, takes up the tune—and then, all whistling, Max, George and Mary enter through the french doors, stop whistling—look at each other in triumph

George Well . . . 'tis done . . . the deed is done.

Mary And done well.

Max And, more to the point—done *together*.

George Jove, yes. I feel the spirit of brotherly togetherness, and, er . . . speaking of spirit, didn't you mention a Napoleon brandy . . . ?

Max I certainly did. (*He produces a decanter and places it on the table and starts to fetch glasses*)

Mary I'm not having you falling into bad habits, George . . .

George I know it's early in the day, dear . . . but it is a rather unusual occasion . . .

Mary Time of day has nothing to do with it—your hands are filthy—and so are mine . . . Just because we've connived at disposing of a body, it's no excuse for us to sink into moral decline. I insist we wash first. And anyway—there are still some things to take care of . . .

George and Max react

Mary The rug—the vase—I like things to be neat.

Max She's right.

George I'm afraid she always is.

Max goes to get the waste-bin, dustpan and brush. He tosses the dust-pan and brush to George—who then sweeps up the broken pieces of the vase and tips them into waste-bin. Mary picks up the rug

Mary (*pausing and looking around*) Is there anything else we may have overlooked?

Max } (*together*) { No.
George }   { Yes.

George Your partner in crime? She'll have to know sooner or later.
Max Of course. (*He starts up the stairs to put the rug back. Then he unlocks the master bedroom door, looks in*) But it's going to be later than sooner. As I thought, she's still asleep ... (*He turns back to them below*) Right then, we'll all go off and wash our handies—and meet you down by the decanter in a few minutes.

Max exits into the master bedroom

George Charming fellow, knew straight away when I saw him.
Mary What about the cunning flick of his eyes?
George Must have been a trick of the light.

George and Mary exit into the guest bedroom

A long pause

Then Suzy appears at the french doors! Then we realize that she IS dead, and Edgar is supporting her damp body. Edgar enters through the french doors, dragging Suzy's body with him. He places it in its original position. He then crosses to the waste-bin, takes it, and spills the broken pieces of vase back in their original position. This done, he surveys the area—then happily goes to pour himself a large glass of ouzo—he sips it—then stops mid-sip as he stares up at the rug on the gallery. Now, drink in hand, he hurries up to the gallery, puts his foot on the rug—pushes it to the floor below. This done, drink in hand—he sidles along the gallery towards the end furthest from the master bedroom door—and happily waits, sipping his drink

A pause. Then Mary enters from the guest bedroom, and briskly crosses to the sink to pick up the soap. She returns again—this time, casually glancing at Suzy's body—and exits into the guest bedroom. The door closes. A pause. Then we hear Mary scream off stage

The guest bedroom door bursts open. Mary and George enter in a rush and stop dead as they stare at Suzy's body. A long, stunned pause

(*Finally,. clearing his throat*) I'm sure there must be a very reasonable explanation.

There is a pause

Don't you think so, dear?

There is a pause—Mary is transfixed

Dear?

There is a pause

Well, please say something.

Mary finally does—she screams again!

The master bedroom door opens and Max enters in a hurry

Max What's going on! (*He sees the body*) Good Lord! (*He starts down the stairs now, leaving the master bedroom door ajar*) Why on earth have you brought her back!?

George We didn't.
Max Well, I didn't—and if you didn't . . . who did?!
Edgar (*from the gallery*) I did.
Max (*a glance*) Oh, that's all right then . . . (*Double-take*) Edgar!

Edgar starts down the stairs, drink in hand

Edgar It's all your fault, Max.
Mary I owe you an apology, George.
George Apology!?
Mary I was standing here thinking it was *your* fault. I mean, let's face it, it usually is!
Max What do you mean, it's my fault!?
Edgar It was *you* who told me I could be a top thriller writer, Max. You encouraged me.
Max What's that got to do with . . . ? (*He indicates the body*)
Edgar I got depressed, Max. I read back over chapter one of my book, and even *I* knew who did it! I got so depressed that I rushed over here to discuss it with you . . . but you were busy. All of you were very busy . . . disposing of bodies, clearing away evidence . . . *making deals*. So I watched, and I listened, and here I am . . . with a deal of my own.
Max Deal?
Edgar I want half.
Max Half?
Mary Half of his, or half of ours?!
Edgar Half of it all.
Mary George. Don't you understand that what he's suggesting would make us junior partners!? No, no, we couldn't agree to that! Could we?
George I'm afraid we may have to.
Max We'd have to talk it over first.

They all look at Max

You've caught us on the hop, Edgar, we must have a chance to talk it over—*in private*. And personally I am far too sensitive to carry on such a conversation with Suzy lying there, so why don't you go and pop her in the woodshed?
Edgar Oh, very well. (*He starts to drag Suzy away*) But there's nothing to talk about.

Edgar exits through the french doors, with Suzy's body

George He's right. There *is* nothing to talk over. I'm afraid it's the short and curlies again, dear.
Max Not yet. Keep smiling—and *talk*.
George } (*together*) { Why?
Mary } } What about?
Max Anything. (*He turns his back to the window and begins to deftly spoon drug powder into the ouzo bottle*) I'll lace the ouzo with this stuff, to make him sleep!
George Ah!

Mary I see.

Max Couple of minutes and he'll be out like a light ... we can dispose of Suzy's body ... *the evidence* ...

Mary And then slip away to Buenos Aires ... pick up our million ...

George Millions, dear, millions! (*He eyes Max admiringly*) Yes, a Chiddingbury man through and through.

Max Keep *smiling!*

Mary I am.

George Yes, I promise you she is—that *is* how she looks when she's smiling!

Max puts the bowl and ouzo down—just in time

  Edgar enters through the french doors

Edgar That's long enough.

Max You're absolutely right, Edgar—and indeed you were absolutely right when you said we had no alternative but to comply with your demand.

Edgar I *told* you.

Max But, Edgar, I do hope this isn't going to mean the end of our friendship ... ?

Edgar Well ... when I get my half I won't be doing any more writing ...

Max Perhaps so ... but at least one last drink together, eh? To show there's no hard feelings?

Edgar That's very big of you, Max.

Max is already pouring two ouzos

Max It's a question of the better man—*the bigger brain*—won out in the end.

Edgar I'll drink to that.

He takes a glass and drains it. Max tosses his (unseen by Edgar) into a bowl or in a plant pot—and immediately recharges Edgar's glass

Max Fine. (*To George and Mary*) And what about you ... a drink, eh? Partners in crime and all that?

George (*picking up and extending a glass*) Right. (*Then he realizes and pulls his glass back*) Ah!

Max No—no—a little brandy for you I thought. (*He moves to pour drink from the decanter into three glasses*) That rare old Napoleon I've been saving for a special occasion ... and this is a special occasion wouldn't you say?

Edgar Brandy? Oh, I think *I'd* rather ... (*He seems about to hand the ouzo glass back*)

Max Don't be excessive, Edgar. You are almost a millionaire now ... go on like this and, before you know it, you'll be back to writing worst-sellers again.

Mary Yes, start as you mean to continue.

Max Right. That's a perfectly good ouzo, drink it and *then* you can have some brandy.

Edgar (*after considering*) Cheers. (*He starts to drink ouzo again*)

Mary, George and Max, glasses in hand, watch him

(*Making a face*) Dunno—this ouzo tastes funny.

Max Sweet. Edgar, it tastes sweet.

Edgar It should. But it doesn't. Tastes funny. Salty.

Max That's the best ouzo money can buy. To my way of thinking, (*to Mary and George*) it's an absolute knock-out.

Edgar (*drinking again*) Yes, I'm getting used to the taste now. (*Suddenly*) But I think I'll have to sit down.

Mary
George } (*together*) Ah!
Max

Edgar sits, smiles up at them

Edgar A millionaire! The thought goes to a man's legs.

Mary Ah, it's working upwards.

Edgar stands up—very brightly

Edgar Feel better. (*He drains his ouzo and bounces to his feet*) And I'm ready for that brandy now.

Mary
Max   (*together*) So am I.
George

They drink their brandy—Max pours some into Edgar's glass

Edgar (*very brightly*) Lovely. Lovely.

Max, Mary and George regard him—then move downstage in a huddle and speak sotto voce

George What's gone wrong?

Mary Did you give him enough?

Max Any more and it would have melted the glass. (*He hurries back to the sugar bowl and dips his finger in it. He tastes his finger*) It's salt!

Note: during this preceding exchange Janet has exited from the bedroom— but hopefully she will not be noticed until:

Janet Yes, my darling!

Max, George, Mary and Edgar turn to stare up to where Janet stands on the gallery. She is fully dressed, and carries a small valise

It *is* salt. It has always been salt. Right from the moment I crept down to your workroom and saw you concocting the stuff. (*She starts to descend into the area*) Hallo, Edgar. You are a big disappointment to me. If you hadn't been greedy you might not be involved in this at all. Greedy—and in particular—greedy with the brandy.

Max (*finally*) Darling . . .

Janet I do wish you wouldn't say that, Max. I'm not your darling. I knew I wasn't your darling a few days ago when I saw Suzy Stevens hanging around the island—dressed up as me, and *rowing*. That's when I *first*

knew you were up to something—that's when I first began to be very wary indeed. (*She moves to pick up the sugar bowl*) Hence the salt. As soon as you finished mixing the drug I swapped it for salt . . . and then I knew you see, that whenever I tasted salt, I had to pretend to go to sleep. And, oh the things I heard when I was pretending to be asleep! The things I saw through half-closed lids. I was scared too. I'm not sure what frightened me most—when you put me in the boat and it started to sink—or when you came rushing back to rescue me! (*She turns to the dumb-founded Edgar*) Oh, Edgar, if *only* you hadn't been greedy! Max tried to drug you too, you know. He drugged your ouzo with this . . . (*She touches the sugar bowl*) But it wasn't the drug at all, you see? Just salt. No, I put the real drug into the brandy!

Max, George, Mary and Edgar all react as they stare at the empty brandy glasses they hold

All The brandy!?
Janet Yes, the brandy. I knew you were planning to drink it—to celebrate *my* inheritance . . .
Max The brandy!? How much did you put in?
Janet All of it, of course.
Max All of it! We'll probably sleep for a week or even longer!
Janet Oh, I'm so glad, I thought only a day at the most.

Now, Max takes a step towards her, and the drug takes effect, he staggers—half falls, supports himself against a piece of furniture. Then Edgar, George and Mary all start to react to the effects of the drug

It does work awfully fast, doesn't it? Well done, Max—you got something right at last. About time—because you got *us* wrong for so very long. You got *me* wrong. I loved you—do you know that? I really did love you.
Max Janet . . . darling . . . I love you.
Janet No, Max—you love money, and intrigue, and yourself—not necessarily in that order.

She regards them—they are all showing increased effects of the drug now

A week or even longer . . . ? Oh, that gives me *plenty* of time.
Mary What are you going to do!?
Janet Row myself back to the mainland, catch the first possible plane to Buenos Aires—pick up my millions and—what was it you said, Max?—live happily ever after.
Max It won't work!
Janet Oh?
Max Your passport—soon as they see it's been tampered with——
Janet (*interjecting*) Silly boy. I'll tell them I lost my passport. They'll be ever so sympathetic and provide a new one—especially when they find out how rich I am.
Mary George . . . do something!
George (*yawning*) Sorry, dear . . . bit tired. Besides—she's got it all worked out—very clever. (*Sudden thought*) I say, you didn't happen to go to Chiddingbury? . . . No, course not.

Janet Sweet dreams then. (*She makes her way to the french doors, then pauses*) Oh, I forgot to mention. Just before I board the plane I shall phone the police—anonymously—and tell them you're here.

Max (*yawning*) But we'll still be dead to the world.

Janet Exactly. They'll have *days* to sit and look at you, and they'll find Suzy's body—smell the brandy—listen to your snoring and ... do you know what conclusion I think they'll come to? That some dreadful, drunken, drugged-up orgy took place and that one of you, or *all of you*, murdered Suzy.

Edgar They'll look for you ... extradite you from Buenos Aires.

Janet Don't be naïve, Edgar—*very* rich people don't get extradited—and certainly not from Buenos Aires. The case may go on for years—while all of you languish in Greek jails. I look forward to reading about it. 'Bye.

Janet exits

Mary, Max, George and Edgar are all in various postures and attitudes—all very close to sleep now

George *Can* she read Portugese?

Mary What!?

George Well, that's what they speak in Buenos Aires, isn't it? Or is it a patois of Portugese?

Edgar We've got to try and stay awake—beat the drug! We've got to walk up and down ...

Max Walk!? I can't even bloody stand!

George Yes, my eyes keep closing and I keep seeing goats. Hundreds of goats jumping over a hedge ... not butting—jumping—quite definitely jumping.

Mary This is awful—terrible ...

Max We are all aware of the predicament, Mrs Ticklewell.

Mary I don't mean that. It's the fact that—George, I have been faithful to you our entire married life—I have never slept with another man ... and now I find myself sleeping with three at once!

Edgar There must be *something* we can do!?

Max It's no use ... we have to resign ourselves to the fact that we're all going to sleep ... and when we wake up—the first thing we'll see is handcuffs!

As he speaks, he collapses—they are all virtually fast asleep now. A beat—and then suddenly George sits right up

George Oh my God!

His tone is such that it causes all the others to stir long enough to raise their heads and look at him

It has just occurred to me. I shall miss the Test Match!

George slumps back again—as do the others. They settle, start to snore as——

—the CURTAIN *slowly falls*

FURNITURE AND PROPERTY LIST

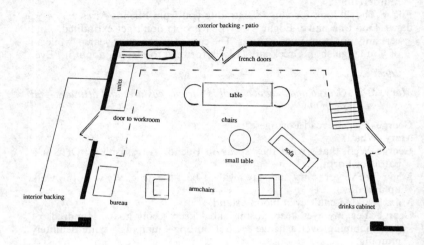

exterior backing - patio

french doors

units

door to workroom

table

chairs

small table

sofa

interior backing

bureau

armchairs

drinks cabinet

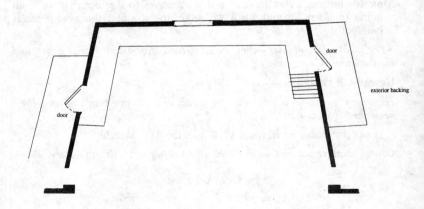

door

door

exterior backing

ACT I

Scene 1

On stage: *Main area:*

Table. *On it:* breakfast things, including bowl of sugar, cereal bowls, spoons, cups, saucers, cornflakes, jug of milk

Chairs

Small sink. *On draining board:* soap, towel. *In cupboard below:* dustpan and brush

Cooker. *On it:* kettle

Fridge

Pantry cupboards. *In them:* glasses, crockery, food

Work surfaces. *On one:* coffee percolator containing coffee (practical, plugged in)

Waste-bin

Sofa

Armchairs

Small bureau. *In drawers:* insurance policy, papers, pens

Drinks cabinet. *In it:* bottles of drink including ouzo, soft drinks, assorted glasses, decanter of brandy

Small table. *On it:* vase

A few items of Greek bric-a-brac, including decorative bowl

Gallery:

Small rug at top of stairs

Small table. *On it:* vase identical to one below

Key in master bedroom door

Window curtains at gallery window

Off stage: Small paper bag containing white powder **(Max)**
Towel **(Suzy)**
Blonde wig **(Suzy)**
2 huge suitcases **(George)**
2 smaller suitcases **(Mary)**

Personal: **Mary:** bunghole in pocket
George: mourning patch, watch fob on chain

Scene 2

Strike: Breakfast things from table
Dirty glass

Set: Bowl on work surface
Blonde wig on table

Off stage: 2 passports **(May)**
Sugar bowl **(Suzy)**
2 bottles of dye **(Suzy)**
2 bottles of ouzo, boxed orchid **(Edgar)**

SCENE 3

Strike:	Dirty glasses
	Blonde wig
Re-set	Rug pushed aside at top of stairs
Set:	Polish, dusters at top of stairs
	Dressing-gown on back of master bedroom door
Off stage:	Glass of ouzo **(George)**
Personal:	**Max:** key in pocket

ACT II

SCENE 1

Re-set:	Rug at top of stairs
	Pieces of broken vase in kitchen waste-bin
Set:	Orange juice in fridge
Off stage:	Bottle of ouzo **(George)**
	Sugar bowl **(Max)**
Personal:	**Suzy:** watch fob
	Max: key in pocket
	George: broken watch chain

SCENE 2

Off stage:	Small valise **(Janet)**
Personal:	**Max:** key in pocket

LIGHTING PLOT

Practical fittings required: pendant light

Interior. A converted farmhouse. The same scene throughout

ACT I, SCENE 1.   Early morning

To open: General early morning light

No cues

ACT I SCENE 2.   Early evening

To open: General early evening light

No cues

ACT I, SCENE 3.   Night

To open: Dim lighting, moonlight coming through french doors and window, lights in workroom, master and guest bedrooms

Cue 1   **Max** puts light on and off in signal   (Page 24)
            Flicker main light on and off

ACT II, SCENE 1.   Morning

To open: General sunny lighting

No cues

ACT II, SCENE 2.   Morning

To open: General sunny lighting

No cues

EFFECTS PLOT

ACT I

Cue 1   **Mary** starts down stairs again and is almost at the bottom   (Page 28)
Loud crack

ACT II

Cue 2   **Max:** "That you survived."   (Page 41)
Clatter from master bedroom

MADE AND PRINTED IN GREAT BRITAIN BY
LATIMER TREND & COMPANY LTD PLYMOUTH

MADE IN ENGLAND